BECOMING
brianna

tip tip tip

TERRI LIBENSON

SCHOLASTIC INC.

wrrrrrr

ISBN 978-1-338-71357-2

12 11 10 9 8 7 6 5 4 3 2 1   20 21 22 23 24 25

Printed in the U.S.A.   40

First Scholastic printing, September 2020

Typography by Terri Libenson and Laura Mock

To the clergy and educators at Fairmount Temple, who helped shape my kids and gave them a home away from home

Author at age 13

wasn't as blurry in real life

hair looked uncombed (but wasn't, I swear)

dressed for big event (by Mom)

nervous, excited, itchy (the days of lace)

PROLOGUE

Well, here I am again. How, how, how did I get myself into this TWICE?

Maybe I'm a glutton for punishment. Or just a sucker. That last one probably nails it. Why else would I put myself in the spotlight again?

Peeking through the curtains, I see my parents and lots of friends. At least I have support.

Or witnesses for this train wreck.

Okay, here I go. I hope I know my part well. I hope I don't screw up. I hope I don't trip on my face. I hope, I hope, I hope . . .

I hope I get this over with FAST.

EIGHT MONTHS AGO

Mom and I are sitting at the kitchen table, shoving pizza in our faces. It's homemade pizza. Mom started making it from scratch when she realized it was just about the only thing I ever ate without complaining. Also, she figured it would be healthier.

It's not bad. I like Ramone's Pizza the best, but I've gotta hand it to Mom. She badgered the owner for the sauce recipe a thousand times until he finally gave in. Ramone made her swear she wouldn't give it away and would burn the photocopy of his hand-written recipe.

I'm at Mom's condo this week. My parents are divorced and share custody. They trade off weeks. It can be a pain going back and forth, but I'm pretty used to it.

Packed stuff I drag along:

favorite clothes (50% PJs)

science books

small fuzzy pillow

phone

backpack full of homework

Camp Robo water bottle

extra pair of tangled earbuds

handy wheels

fluffy key chain thingy

hidden candy (shh!)

childhood stuffed animal (also shh!)

missing arm

Anyway, here I sit, stuffing myself with pizza. At least, I try.

Did I mention she is the Queen of Guilt?

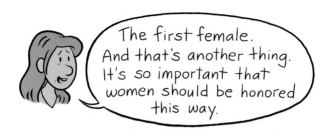

That is the **ultimate** guilt. Mom knows I've been a feminist since I was, like, five. She just touched a nerve.

So fast, I almost don't see her get up, Mom races over and engulfs me in a powerful hug.

What Mom doesn't know is that any time she says that . . .

. . . I usually do.

LaVEURNE FINISHES AND STEPS BACK.

EIGHT MONTHS AGO

So, by now you might be wondering what exactly I just agreed to. If you're twelve or thirteen years old and Jewish, you've probably guessed.

Yep, I just agreed to have a bat mitzvah.

Kids have bar or bat mitzvahs ("bar" for boys, "bat" for girls) around age thirteen (sometimes younger for girls 'cause, you know, we're mature and stuff). It marks a "coming of age" in Jewish tradition. The boy or girl leads the service—in Hebrew!—usually at a synagogue in front of family, friends, and even strangers (aka relatives you've never met).

This is no little thing, believe me. You have to start preparing about six months ahead. Or longer, if you don't know Hebrew too well. Which I don't.

Here's the story. My mom is Jewish; my dad isn't. Traditionally, this means I'm considered Jewish. If it were reversed, I wouldn't be. Weird, considering the usual religious patriarchy* thing.

*(men in charge, big surprise)

Traditional view

Jewish   not   not
        Jewish Jewish

not   Jewish Jewish
Jewish

Nontraditional view*

*(our temple, in a nutshell)

Jewish   not   Jewish
       Jewish

not   Jewish Jewish
Jewish

not   Jewish Jewish
Jewish

When I was growing up, Mom **encouraged** me to go to religious school (aka made me). That meant a couple weeknights and Sunday mornings. Because my studies came first, I didn't always have time to go.

And **maybe** I used that as an excuse once too often.

> I have a science quiz and...um... recorder practice.

It's not that it was horrible. The teachers were nice, and they tried to make the lessons interesting, like with games and stuff. But most of the kids went to the local Jewish day camp during summers and were used to hanging out together. I didn't go to that camp, so I always felt a little left out.

gurgle

science camp

"Rosie"

bow

wrrrrrr

robotics camp

Also, I was pretty bad at Hebrew.

I know what you're thinking: me, bad at a class? But languages aren't my thing. I'm not even that great at Spanish. I just study extra hard for it, and that's how I get As.

Anyway, I put my foot down and stopped going to religious school after fifth grade. I had way more important things to do, and I really wasn't that into it. Dad couldn't care less.

Mom agreed and seemed to stop pressing the issue.

But around September, she brought up the idea of a bat mitzvah. At first, I was like:

But she kept insisting. And insisting. And . . .

So here I am wondering—not for the first time—what I just got myself into.

It's true. Mom was the first girl in her family to have a bat mitzvah. Her temple didn't allow 'em for girls until then. Even her older sister, my aunt Dani, didn't have one. (Her younger sister, my aunt Ashley, was just plain against it, for some reason.)

I know Mom just wants me to carry on the tradition she started. I can't really blame her. I'm her only child, so this is her one big chance.

I also know I'm doing this more for her than me.

But . . .

. . . I'm still trying to figure out **why**.

GETTING A LATE LUNCH.

So, do you want to talk about something else? Help take your mind off it?

I dunno.

Well, your hair looks so pretty. LaVeurne did a great job.

Yeah...

WE EAT IN SILENCE.

I remember my big day, so long ago—

Mom? Can you *not?*

Oh, sure, hon.

I FEEL BAD, BUT HONESTLY—
IF EITHER OF US STARTS
TALKING, I MIGHT EXPLODE.

SUPERWOMAN:

Nerves of Steel

ME:

Nerves of Silly Putty

WE FINISH UP AND GET GOING.

SEVEN MONTHS AGO

Em and I are at lunch. It's pretty loud today. Everyone's excited because Thanksgiving break starts tomorrow. The enthusiasm is echoed by the force of the ice cream freezer lid slamming.

art club kids

Emo girl

SLAMMO

table earthquake

I make a face at Emmie's lunch.

She pokes one with her spork.

It's hard not to make fun of Emmie's lunches, which are usually leftovers from home. Her mom's kind of a health nut. "Nut" being the key word.

But I know Em's **so** over it, so I try not to push it.

I bite into my sandwich. I'm attempting to branch out from pizza. Dad packed me his leftover sub from a faculty meeting yesterday. Turkey with gravy, of course.

I immediately spit it out.

I sip my milk.

Joe Lungo grabs three ice cream sandwiches and slams the freezer lid so hard, my turkey and gravy separate.

The chatty art club kids get up and leave.

lone olive

Tyler Ross suddenly runs by our table and tries to catch a flying Styrofoam plate. It misses and lands in front of us.

gray, lumpy, and slimy
(probably gravy)

Hey, sorry!
I'll get that.

He grabs the greasy plate and flings it at Anthony Randall. They're playing some kind of Frisbee game with Joe L. They're each in a corner of the cafeteria in triangle formation. Except they're trying to eat ice cream sandwiches and play at once. Not very effective.

keeps landing
on tables

keeps landing
outside mouths

#epic

The lunch monitor must be on break. I turn toward Emmie,
whose face is bright violet.

two shades
above normal
blushing

Maybe you should
tell him you like him.
And if he doesn't
like you back, at least
you can move on.

Stop it. You're not
changing the subject.
Back to the bat
mitzvah.

Okay, okay.
So yeah, I
decided to do it.
Mainly for my mom.

Oh, Briii.

Like you should talk. How many half marathons has your mom dragged you to?

To watch, not to <u>do</u>.

Okay, fine. I guess I can take it back and not have one. But a small part of me wants to, I think. I don't know why.

Maybe underneath, you have a spiritual side.

SNORT

Yeah, that's it.

Maybe you'll figure it out as you go along.

Maybe.

The plate lands in front of us again, this time knocking over my milk. I jump up. Luckily there's not much in the carton. It dribbles down the side of the table and just misses my shoes.

This time Anthony rushes over and grabs the plate, half an ice cream sandwich sticking out of his mouth.

Now it's my turn to blush.

I feel myself turning the same shade of violet. Yeah, okay, I deserved that. Still, I won't admit it.

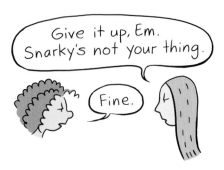

We look at each other and burst out laughing. At the same time, some lone girl passes us, balancing an overflowing lunch tray. (How'd she score **three** tacos? I mean, yuck, but still . . .)

Ooh! Don't people have parties right after a bat mitzvah? You should invite Anthony. And then you could invite Tyler Ross. An' then we could dance right next to them.

(SNORT) Like that would ever happen. And since when do you dance?

I did at the sixth-grade dance.

And you almost fell on Lindsay Donsky. Oh, that could be your plan! Trip over Tyler. He'd have to catch you. Then when you're in his arms, he'd find you irresistible! That's called "meeting cute."

I already know him, silly.

I look across the room at Anthony. He just sat down and is avoiding the lunchroom monitor, who finally showed up. He spits into his napkin. I still don't know why that doesn't gross me out. I guess love really is blind.

WE ARRIVE AT THE TEMPLE.

DAD'S COMING LATER. HE HAS TO PICK UP SOME THINGS FOR THE PARTY ROOM.

TOP SECRET

MOM AND I WALK IN. ON ONE HAND, IT'S TOTAL CHAOS.

party room

ON THE OTHER...

tumbleweed

Atrium

MOM'S PHONE STARTS BUZZING.

Oh shoot, it's Grandma.

Hi, Mom.

THERE'S NOT MUCH FOR ME TO DO YET, SO I WANDER DOWN THE HALL.

old consecration photos

There I am!

me, age 6

MAN, I WAS CUTE!

dish eyes

asymmetrical pigtails 'cause I used to tug on the left one

little baby teeth

preppy white dress

BRIANNA DAVIS

I ACTUALLY REMEMBER THAT TIME, 'CAUSE IT WAS RIGHT AFTER WE MOVED TO LAKEFRONT FROM ATLANTA.

looking closely, I might be able to see tears of homesickness

squint

CONSECRATION MARKS THE BEGINNING OF JEWISH LEARNING. BUT I DIDN'T CARE ABOUT THAT.

I just wanna go back home.

IT WAS BEFORE MY PARENTS GOT DIVORCED. WE HAVE SOME PHOTOS OF US ON THAT DAY.

(did this when I was nervous)

I WONDER IF I EVEN KNEW WHAT I COMMITTED TO BACK THEN. AND THAT I'D END UP HERE TODAY.

doubtful

kinda wish LaVeurne had given me pigtails

tug tug

SIX MONTHS AGO

I'm hanging out by Emmie's locker. It's right before homeroom, and the hallway's crowded.

(taking eyes off Tyler)

Em finishes shoving art supplies in her backpack and grabs her book. She closes her locker door, and we walk by Joe Lungo and Tyler. Actually, I have to step over Joe Lungo because he's rolling on the floor and howling like a dog.

We stop around the corner from homeroom.

I don't know what my mom is planning for this party, but I'm sure she's going overboard. She's, like, in full theatrics mode. If she could, she'd probably hire the entire cast of *Hamilton* to be dance motivators.

What're those?

People who lead everyone on the dance floor and show them moves. I was googling stuff about bat mitzvahs and found it.

Maybe she'll build a stage and sing by herself.

DON'T even joke about that.

Across the hall, we see Em's new friend from art class, Sarah. She waves and comes over. I feel a little pang inside, like a hand just squeezed my guts.

Hi, guys. Em, did you see the Zentangles hung up outside Ms. Laurie's room? She put 'em next to our self-portraits.

Em. Now they're on shortened-name terms. That's when you know people are getting to be good friends.

Yeah. Ugh, that's so embarrassing. I hate my self-portrait.

Are you kidding? It's the best one in the class!

I want to gag. But I hold it in because the bell's about to ring, and I realize we're gonna be late for homeroom. That's a good excuse to nudge Em away from Sarah.

I tug on her sweater sleeve.

She throws me an annoyed look. I keep forgetting myself.

We walk toward homeroom, and I try to put all this bat mitzvah and Sarah stuff behind me. For now.

Someone taps me on the shoulder.

Emmie and I do a double take. Zoe Torres is one of the coolest kids in our grade. Popular but not too popular. She's pretty friendly, which is one of the reasons why people like her. But it's the first time she's ever spoken to me.

That was nice . . . but weird. No one's ever congratulated me on getting an A before. Usually I get a reaction like:

Emmie and I shrug at the same time and walk into homeroom.

WE'RE BACK IN THE ATRIUM.
I GET THE SUDDEN FEELING
I FORGOT SOMETHING.

Mom. No, Mom, we don't need extra sweaters for the sanctuary. It's like a hundred degrees. Mom.

?

THERE'S MORE COMMOTION
COMING FROM THE PARTY ROOM,
BUT THE DOORS ARE CLOSED.

Fine. Just bring them. *I DON'T CARE WHAT SIZE!*

feel like a volcano of nerves about to erupt

cantor

A MINUTE LATER:

Okay, it's fine. Dad was on his way, but he turned around to get your speech and notes. On the kitchen table, right?

← nodding

MOM'S PHONE RINGS AGAIN.

Are you okay?

nodding again

Okay. Hello? Oh, hey, Ash. Yes, fine, tell Mom I'll check the thermostat again....

I WANDER OVER TO ANOTHER PART OF THE ATRIUM AND SIT ON A BENCH. I TRY TO BREATHE.

Cough! cough!

somehow choking on own spit

I'M PANICKING AGAIN. BUT I CAN'T LOOK LIKE I'M PANICKING 'CAUSE THAT'LL MAKE MOM ERUPT LIKE VESUVIUS.

Sure, I can remember Vesuvius, but I can't remember anything else.

OKAY, MOM'S BUSY. DAD'S STILL GONE. I NEED SOMEBODY.

Somebody else.

text text text text

FIVE MONTHS AGO

I'm at the temple, sitting in Cantor Jordana Caruso-Sager's office (fun to say ten times fast). I just (barely) got through practicing the first of many Hebrew blessings. On the plus side, I think I'm now reading at a second-grade level.

It's okay. It's an especially tough language, and considering you weren't a regular at religious school, this is pretty good.

pang of guilt

I'm supposed to meet with the cantor about three or four times before the bat mitzvah so she can see how I'm coming along with the prayers. This is our first meeting, and I'm not exactly shining.

fsssttttt

more like fizzling

Okay, Bri, let's move on.

She hands me a prayer book earmarked with little fluorescent sticky notes.

This is the Torah portion, or parashah, for your bat mitzvah. I'd like you to read over the English translation and find three paragraphs that have meaning for you.

That's the section you'll read in Hebrew on The Big Day.

It's a good one, Bri! It's a celebration, all about the holiday of Shavuot. It talks about the giving of the Torah to our ancestors.

It's basically an agreement between our people and God.

Inwardly I groan. Because, honestly, I don't even know if I believe in any of this. So does this mean my bat mitzvah will just be one big sham?

 Are you okay?

 Oh... yeah.

Okay. We'll also set up a meeting with Rabbi Nosanchuk to start outlining your speech, which is based on this *Torah* portion.

 A... a speech?

(chuckle) It'll be okay, Bri. It's not as bad as you think. He'll help you — especially at first.

Inwardly I groan again. A speech? It's bad enough I have to get up in front of everyone and chant Hebrew. Making a speech just adds to the . . . the . . .

pile of dread

I must look exactly how I feel because Cantor Caruso-Sager chuckles louder.

Don't worry, all our kids pull through.

Easy for her to say. Besides, there's always a first.

She gives me one final little pep talk, and then we say goodbye.

Dad's waiting for me in the hall. I'm relieved he's here instead of Mom. She's been in hyper-planning mode and won't stop talking about seating charts. You'd think I was getting married.

We walk to his car.

He's trying to make me feel better, but at the same time, part of me wonders why he never encouraged me to come here more often.

Oh geez, now I sound like Mom.

Anyway, how could he have known I was gonna do this?

We get in the car and start driving.

I must have a horrified look on my face because he stops himself.

I squeeze my eyes shut. Both my parents are teachers, which means they don't earn the highest salaries. Proven by all the stuff they make by hand.

Mom's threadbare homemade curtains

loose string

Dad's questionable deck

sproing

Great. Now I add "feel guilty" to the top of my to-do list. I ask myself for the fourteen hundredth time this month:

Why am I having a bat mitzvah?

MY DAD ARRIVES, LOOKING (AS USUAL) LIKE HE JUST WOKE UP.

shirt half-tucked

Here, Bri. Please tell me I grabbed the right papers.

bagel-'n'-lox tie untied

YES! Thank you!!

Oh, Ben! Thank goodness. We've got another issue with the caterer.

(groan) Why do we need a caterer, anyway?

Can't you just be supportive?

This is me being supportive.

THEY BICKER WHILE I SIT THERE AND TRY TO BLEND IN TO A HUGE POTTED PLANT.

Can we please take this into the party room and away from everyone else?

Who's everyone? Bri and a ficus?

AS USUAL, DAD ARGUES BUT FOLLOWS HER. I SIT FOR A MINUTE, TRYING TO REMEMBER ALL THE HEBREW I JUST LOST.

Mom and Dad heading to party room

FOUR MONTHS AGO

Emmie's over. We're hanging in my room.

I get it. I'm used to Em sketching me, anyway. It probably **would** make me less jittery.

I start reading my Hebrew blessings. I stumble a lot, but I keep going. At the same time, Emmie draws me in her sketchbook. That thing is full of **mes**. I don't mind; she only does it to practice her faces, and she sure wouldn't dare draw anyone else except her family.

Although . . . I once snuck a peek at her book while she was in the bathroom and saw a few sketches from memory of Tyler. They weren't half bad. I was surprised she hadn't put little hearts in his eyes and floating around his head. That girl is a **goner**.

But I should talk. If I could draw Anthony, I totally would. I don't even have the nerve to sneak selfies with him in the background, like a lot of girls with crushes do. (Which, by the way, is **so** obvious!)

I finish the four blessings. Em looks up.

That was good.

Nah, it wasn't.

Well, I couldn't tell, except, for, like, five times. Anyway, most of your friends aren't Jewish and wouldn't care.

But my family would. And I do have some Jewish friends.

You do? Who?

A bunch from robotics camp. And my mom's friends' kids that I hung out with when I was younger.

Plus some family friends from Atlanta that are coming. I'm on SnapGab with 'em. This is gonna be almost half and half. Just like me.

Oh. Wow. Well then, keep going.

That's it. I haven't even learned my Torah portion. Those are just the "before and after" blessings.

My dad knocks on the door.

RAP
RAP

Come in.

Hi, Emmie. Bri, you left your phone in the kitchen. It started buzzing.

Oh, thanks.

He raises an eyebrow at all the books and old clothes scattered like mulch across the floor but doesn't say anything, which I'm grateful for. I know I have to get rid of some of it already.

eyebrow says more than words

He raises a hand to signal goodbye and leaves.

That is the weirdest of weird. I mean, I know we have a test in a couple days, but this is the first time Zoe T. ever asked **me** for help. And I thought she was okay at math.

Still . . . wow. Kinda flattering.

That is so weird.

Well, this algebra chapter is pretty hard, so maybe she just needs some help.

Me and annoying Dev Devar are the only ones who ace this class. And I doubt she'd ever go to him. He'd make her memorize mnemonic rap lyrics.

I text back.

k. when do u want 2 meet?

 tomrrw at my house aftr school? No wait, got soccer. Like 7?

k. send address.

 cool!!! u r best!

tak
tappa
tap
click

I stare at my phone for a sec, then toss it casually on my bed. It slides off into a pile of dirty clothes.

So weird. But also kind of exciting. I'm not caught up in coolness or anything, but I have to admit: studying with Zoe gives me a little thrill-chill.

I start to wonder what her house looks like.

Then I start to wonder if we could become friends.

I look at Em, hunched over her sketchbook like an armadillo while she scratches away again. I think of her and Sarah in art class, bonding over landscapes.

Maybe it wouldn't be the worst thing to try and branch out a little.

OMG, I JUST UPCHUCKED ON MY BAT MITZVAH DAY.

Is this a really gross omen?

I SPLASH SOME WATER ON MY FACE AND TAKE A FEW SMALL SIPS. THEN I SIT ON A COUCH IN THE LADIES' LOUNGE.

older than me

spring poking my butt

THE ONLY GOOD THING ABOUT GETTING SICK IS THAT IT TAKES YOUR MIND OFF FEELING NERVOUS.

BEFORE: focused on Hebrew

NOW: focused on keeping rest of lunch down

Bri? You look pale as a sheet. You okay?

Um, I've been better.

Anyway, it was fine, but I swore I wouldn't do it again.

And I just threw up. Ick. Sorry.

An' now here I am... and I have to do everything in Hebrew. An' give a <u>speech</u>. And—

First of all, don't apologize. It's natural to be nervous. Second, do you need anything? Crackers? Ginger Ale?

shaking head

Third, you've got this, Brianna Davis. And if not, I'll be up there to help you. So will the rabbi. Heck, you wouldn't be the first to throw up before a bat mitzvah.

I once had a kid vomit in the middle of her parashah right in the pulpit flowers.

Really?

Well, maybe to the side of them a little. The custodian wasn't pleased.

I LAUGH AND FEEL BETTER.

Sure you're okay?

Yeah.

Want me to stick around?

No, I'm good.

AND PRACTICALLY CRY WITH RELIEF!

THREE MONTHS AGO

I've stopped talking about the bat mitzvah at school. Trying to stop thinking about it, too. It's been getting in the way of everything. Hebrew tutoring and practice take up so much time. I need to . . . What's that word? Compartmentalize.

I did take a break from it for a day when Mom roped me into doing the talent show.

I won't even go into **that**. Let's just say it did not help my bat mitzvah jitters. Okay, it was kinda fun, and I actually got a (surprising) friend out of it.

Dev

But it also reminded me that I **hate** being the center of attention. Besides, it's one thing to memorize a bunch of lines and act 'em out. . . . It's another to—

Oh, forget it. **Compartmentalizing.**

It's the end of the day, and I'm grabbing everything from my locker.

Everyone and their sister are buying ukuleles now. It's the latest nerd rage (after nerd glasses). I like to say I had one before it became trendy.

The final bell rings, and we head to our buses. Sarah waves bye and gets on hers. Em and I get on ours. We sit in our usual seats.

When Em gets nervous, everything she says sounds like a question.

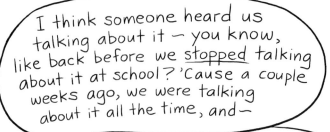

I think someone heard us talking about it — you know, like back before we _stopped_ talking about it at school? 'Cause a couple weeks ago, we were talking about it all the time, and —

Yeah, I get it. So what's the rumor?

People think it's gonna be this huge blowout.

WHAT?

You know how rumors travel through school — it's like a game of Telephone. I overheard the Gossip Girls talking.

People think it's gonna be *the* summer experience, and now some kids wanna score an invite. One kid called it "Briannapalooza."

There are rumors of Drake coming and a huge Dippin' Dots truck.

My jaw drops. Then I start laughing hysterically because it's so over-the-top.

That's pure craziness.

I know, but now everyone's googling bat mitzvah parties, and of course all they see are, like, the celebrity ones.

I...uh... am wondering if that's why Zoe is suddenly hanging around you?

getting nervous again

Okay, girl, you just lost your mind.

I'm serious, Bri! I mean, *I* know you're great an' everything. But Zoe is pretty popular, an' all of a sudden, she's, like, your new bff?

I don't think she's interested in finding a new friend like you. No offense.

The bus stops and I get up.

Even she seems surprised by her bluntness. Back in December, she stood up for herself in front of Joe Lungo. After that, she gained some confidence and two new friends, Sarah and Tyler. Ever since, Emmie's been trying to live her "truth." But that's **her** truth.

I get off and don't even turn around to look back at Em through the bus window.

The **nerve!** Yeah, okay, I may not be top tier. But I'm not a social pariah either! Maybe Emmie's just jealous that I'm starting to hang out with Zoe. But it's not like **she** hasn't branched out.

And anyway, I'm not "suddenly" friends with Zoe. We studied together a bunch of times, and it's been growing from there. We text. We watch **Doctor Who**. We're becoming friends. It's not magic; it's just natural.

My thoughts bounce between disbelieving those crazy party rumors and being mad at Emmie.

thoughtnado

I stomp home. I can't remember the last time I was so steamed. Even when she lost a love letter I wrote to Anthony at school in December. I mean, that was an accident. (An' I don't even think I like him anymore.) But this?

This is just . . .

. . . mean.

Something I never knew Emmie had in her.

AUNT ASHLEY REMINDS ME OF A YOGA INSTRUCTOR EMMIE'S MOM ONCE DRAGGED US TO.

AS WE SIT, I FEEL MY PULSE SLOW DOWN. I WISH I COULD BRING HER TO SCHOOL SOMETIMES.

AFTER A WHILE, THOUGH, THE SILENCE GETS TO ME.

Aunt Ash, Mom said you never had a bat mitzvah. Why?

Oh. Well, we weren't particularly religious. We only went to services on High Holidays.

And truthfully, I've always been an atheist, even then. So I put my foot down. Probably the only time I did.

Oh.

But your Mom had a bat mitzvah and was happy about it. It's different for everyone.

At one point, I told her I didn't want to do it.

Yeah? Why?

shrug

I didn't think it had enough meaning for me. I thought it meant more to _her_.

AUNT ASH NODS HER HEAD LIKE SHE GETS IT. BUT THEN...

I think your mom was right about you doing this. Shocking, I know. But I think there's meaning in it for you, Bripee. You can find meaning in a soup can. So this day should knock your socks off.

TWO AND THREE-QUARTER MONTHS AGO

I'm sitting on the deck steps at my dad's. We finally got the patio all set for spring.

furniture hosed down

old lemonade can tossed

loose plank fixed

new weed

I'm rolling a disgusting tennis ball with my foot. It got into the yard by accident. Probably belongs to the neighbor's dog.

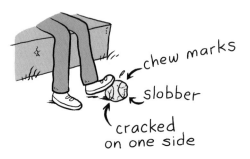

chew marks

slobber

cracked on one side

This is usually where I come out to think. My bedroom is my thinking room all winter, but as soon as warm weather hits, I come out here. Even my brain needs some air.

think

Besides, my room is getting too distracting with all the home-work, STEM stuff, and Hebrew notes spread everywhere. Not to mention the books and clothes that I still haven't done anything with.

I feel really depressed. It's been a week since Emmie and I have spoken to each other. This is the longest we've ever been apart. I haven't been this lonely since, well . . .

The ball slips away and rolls downhill into a hedge separating our yard from the neighbor's. A furry paw suddenly pokes out of the hedge and pulls in the ball. They both disappear.

The thing is, I may be lonely, but I'm also mad. Hopping mad! And for me, that always beats lonely. Because there's usually a valid reason behind "mad." You can't argue with data.

scientist

official-looking pointer

SAD
MAD

facts

I texted both Dev and Zoe the day after Em and I had our fight. I guess I needed some friends.

Zoe came over, which kinda surprised me. She usually likes to hang at her house. (I get it, it's pretty posh.)

Mostly we hung out and watched TV. She briefly tried to cheer me up.

After that, we really didn't say much. But she tried.

Dev came over the next day. Funny how I used to think he was annoying. Things sure have changed.

He's a good listener. Especially over ice cream.

What kills me, though, is that Emmie is spending more time with Sarah, and I know I'm quickly being replaced. Which actually makes me madder! And doesn't exactly help the situation.

The back door opens.

Dad comes over and sits next to me on the steps.

Actually, he didn't. But the last thing I need is a "back in my day" story.

We sit quietly for a moment.

As usual, the silence gets to me.

What? You did?

Yeah. After about a week and one brutal prank of freezing a Mentos in an ice cube and sticking it in his soda.

AHHH!

soda bomb

(chuckle) That's not exactly a good role model story, Dad.

No, but I just wanted to let you know that people can be dumb, and hurtful, and sometimes it's good to cool off... and get back to where you were.

You can't stand Uncle Ryan.

Yes, but we still got back to a better place after I forgave him.

You mean got even with him?

That, too.

I smile, but I'm still not ready to forgive Emmie.

I think about it, but only for a second.

We stand up and are about to head back inside when something shoots out of the hedges.

I don't believe in signs, but maybe that's one. Like, you get what you give, and maybe **that's** Emmie's anger rolling back to me.

Or maybe it's time for the neighbors to get their dog a new ball.

IT'S AN HOUR UNTIL THE SERVICE. DEV SITS WITH ME WHILE I IGNORE THE DRAMA IN THE PARTY ROOM.

Aunt Ashley and Aunt Dani playing referee between parents

What's going on in there?

World War Three. Or something about table placement.

That's what it was ten minutes ago.

WE LISTEN A MOMENT. IT'S A LITTLE CALMER FOR NOW.

So I need you to coach me, like you did during the talent show.

What do you mean?

a few decibels lower

I need tricks so I won't faint or throw up or freeze like last time.

Oh. Well, you could do that old trick of picturing the audience in their underwear.

Er, never mind.

Anyway, you could do some meditation stuff... or visualize the outcome. But one thing your mom once said that stuck out to me...

...is to remember that stage fright usually comes from not having self-confidence. An' the best way to fight that is to be prepared.

TWO AND A HALF MONTHS AGO

Just got ice cream with Dev at Taystee's.

You know you're upset when you've been getting a lot of ice cream lately

Ever since the talent show, we've been hanging out more. Especially now that Em and I aren't speaking to each other.

It's been two weeks. Em tried telling me her side of things again, but I'm still mad and I know how to hold a grudge. Besides, she did **not** apologize.

I stop.

Dev stops a little behind me, like he's scared to catch up.

I start marching in long angry strides. Dev sprints to catch up.

I slow down, but I don't stop brooding.

I keep marching in long strides, with Dev doing little leaps to keep up. We're the same height, but my legs are probably five inches longer.

A leg comparison:

winner

I smile at his efforts. I can't help it. Dev can be annoying, but it's hard to stay mad at him.

But what's harder . . .

lost in thought

sigh

. . . is wondering if he might make sense.

IT'S HALF AN HOUR BEFORE
THE SERVICE STARTS.
HALF AN HOUR.

I'M IN THE RABBI'S OFFICE, WHICH HAS A SECRET DOOR AND HALL THAT LEAD RIGHT TO THE SANCTUARY STAGE. HE SHOWED IT TO ME LAST TIME.

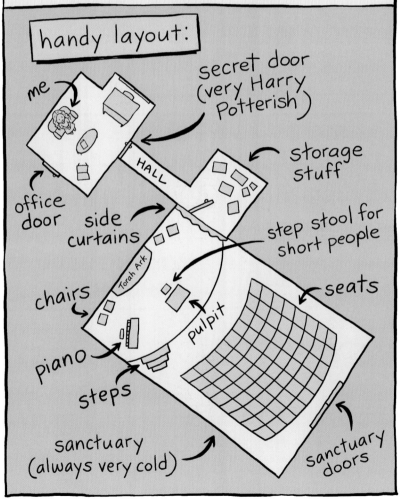

handy layout:

me

secret door (very Harry Potterish)

office door

side curtains

HALL

storage stuff

step stool for short people

Torah Ark

chairs

seats

piano

pulpit

steps

sanctuary (always very cold)

sanctuary doors

I TIPTOE DOWN THE HALL AND PEEK OUT AGAIN.

some relatives (Gram, aunts, and a few first cousins) getting the good seats

I STILL DON'T SEE EMMIE OR ZOE.

chewing on finger-nails

I DO SEE MOM AND DAD. THEY FINALLY STOPPED ARGUING. GUESS MY AUNTS PUT THEM IN THEIR CORNERS.

RABBI NOSANCHUK STILL ISN'T HERE. I RETURN TO HIS OFFICE AND SIT LIKE A FROZEN STATUE.

block of ice

(Could be nerves. Could be the overused air-conditioning)

Where is he?

Maybe he got sick.

Maybe he'll have to cancel this whole thing!

THE CLOCK TICKS. ONLY FIFTEEN MINUTES TO GO.

TWO MONTHS AGO

I'm sitting at the kitchen table at my dad's, trying to tackle my bat mitzvah speech. I'm purposely doing it here 'cause I need to get away from my mom, who continues to drive me batty.

It's been a rough month. Em and I still aren't talking. She's always hanging with Sarah. (By the way, doesn't she have any other friends?) Every time I think about making up with Emmie, I either see them together or think about them doing the same stuff we used to.

The one bright spot: ever since I got friendly with Zoe and Olivia, a lot of other kids in school have noticed. They're acting nicer and friendlier to me, too. Between all the friendliness and the bat mitzvah party hype, I'm suddenly . . . almost . . .

It's a strange feeling. And kinda exhilarating.

"Winn Word of the Week"

(Mrs. Winn, English teacher)

Anyway, I decided to put my fears about Zoe to rest. So we don't have a lot in common—that's natural in the beginning of a friendship, right? Anyway, Zoe texts me all the time. If this is her way of using me . . .

snicker

...then it's a strange way of showing it.

funny meme

The not-so-bright spot: I don't have time to enjoy any of this. I've got so much going on. Like homework. And my hyperfocused mom. And all the Hebrew. And this speech, which I've made no real progress with.

I've tried. Well, once. I met with the rabbi, and we started working on it together. He gave me the whole overview of the Torah portion. The big takeaway is the line from the ancient Jews to God: "We will do and we will hear." Which basically amounts to: "I will blindly follow you."

Part of me thinks:

The other part of me thinks:

I groan and ball up my umpteenth sheet of paper, which my dad won't be happy about. He wants me to type this on his laptop, but I always work better writing on plain, old-school computer paper (aka "forest murdering").

Okay, one more time. I read to myself from the prayer book. It contains many, many, **many** paragraphs about thunder, lightning, dense clouds, smoke, blasts of horns, and mountains trembling . . .

. . . all because people are getting their town laws and tax codes.

Not only that, they decide to just accept it all. Blindly. Without questioning anything.

Okay, so there's more to it. They also receive the Ten Commandments—which I guess deserves all that dramatic fanfare. Those are the biggies. The huge moral codes: Do not kill, blah, blah, blah. But even some of those I've already broken, so how can I get on board with them?

I start to ask if he thinks this whole thing is a good idea. But I change my mind. I don't know if I wanna know the answer. It's too late, anyway. I'm committed.

RABBI NOSANCHUK'S WHISTLING SOUNDS FAMILIAR. I RECOGNIZE IT AS A CARDI B SONG. I LAUGH.

about 70 years old

still a kid at heart

Ready?

As I'll ever be.

You can do better than that.

Just nervous.

…

I threw up an hour ago.

Well, you look tip-top now. I've seen worse. Much worse.

Really?

I once had a bat mitzvah kid get up there and freeze. Not just freeze, but stand frozen for— I kid you not — a full minute.

Which feels like a lifetime when you're up at the pulpit.

What happened?

The cantor and I nodded at her, mouthed the words, you name it. Nothing. We thought she would turn and run. I never saw such stage fright in a kid.

She was as green as lettuce. It's a miracle <u>she</u> didn't throw up.

Eventually something clicked and she began. She stumbled a little at first, but in the end, she knocked it out of the park.

Still, it was touch and go for literally a minute.

I SMILE, BUT STILL FEEL NERVOUS.

unconvincing smile

THE RABBI DOES SOMETHING UNEXPECTED. HE TAKES OUT HIS PHONE.

Selfie time!

Huh?

It's tradition! Well, as of five years ago. Mitzvah kid takes a selfie with the rabbi. We post it on the temple page.

170

Good. <u>Now</u> we're loosened up. And just in time.

HE LEADS ME BACK TO THE CURTAIN. I CAN HEAR THE CROWD MURMURING.

Showtime, Bina.

THAT'S MY HEBREW NAME. IT MEANS "UNDER-STANDING AND WISDOM"...

...A COUPLE THINGS I COULD USE RIGHT NOW.

ONE MONTH AGO

I'm on my way to lunch. Meeting Dev. I've been sitting with him and a few other kids from Science Club.

It's finally May. And unusually hot. **And** there's no air-conditioning.

(hallway smells like combo of Axe and armpit)

I see Zoe and Olivia walking from the opposite end of the hall, and I wave. For a split second, it looks like they saw me and pretended they didn't, but then they wave and smile, all friendly.

I think they're going to stop and talk, but they keep going. Guess they're in a hurry. Seems like that's been happening a lot lately.

At the same time, Zoe's still sending me plenty of SnapGab messages.

It's so confusing.

I invited her and Olivia to the bat mitzvah. When Zoe got the invite, she texted me this.

At first, it made me happy that she was so excited. She kept asking me questions.

She only asked me about the party and the people, not about the ceremony, which was a little weird. But then, that's Zoe. She likes excitement.

I couldn't tell her much 'cause my mom is still keeping everything a secret.

off-limits party doors

STOP

TOP SECRET

NO ENTRY

That means you, Bri!!

Emmie was right about one thing, though. There are still rumors flying around about my "blowout event." I think the last one I heard from Dev was that Shawn Mendes is going to make a surprise appearance by zip-lining into the party room.

As soon as I walk into the cafeteria, I see Emmie and Sarah sitting in our (old) usual spot.

They look at me
and then turn away

It's now been a month. Sarah tried to get us to talk once, but by then Emmie and I were both so mad at each other, it felt too late.

It hits me. Finally. Is it **really** over?

Honestly, I don't even know if I'm mad anymore. I don't know **anything**.

Soon, we see Zoe and Olivia sit at their usual table. To my sur-prise, Zoe waves me over. Usually, they like to eat quickly and then head to the yearbook room. They're both on the committee. They also hate the cafeteria.

cool kids

not sure what to do with hands

giggle

But I mean, like, about the chocolate fountain and Dippin' Dots, and the huge pop band and stuff?

Uhh, no. It's not gonna be anything like that. I mean, I don't know what my mom is planning, but we can't really afford anything too fancy.

Oh.

There is literally dead silence.

Olivia finally clears her throat, and Zoe snaps back to life from her zombie state.

Guess I've been dismissed. I sit back down across from Dev.

For a minute, I thought you were ditching me.

Nope. It kinda feels like I've been ditched, though.

What do you mean?

I dunno. They're nice to me, and we still do stuff. But our friendship seems kinda... off.

It's like they wanna be friends but also... don't.

I've never seen Dev look like this. Angry and serious at once. The same look he had when we were performing a drama scene in the talent show.

He means business.

I watch Zoe and Olivia get up. I catch their eye and wave bye. They wave back, but this time not so enthusiastically.

My sponge brain finally kicks in, and it's like a spotlight shines on my memories.

And:

And:

I know you're great an' everything. But Zoe is pretty popular, an' all of a sudden, she's, like, your new bff?

Over the last couple months, kids I barely know have come up to me and asked how they could get an invitation to my bat mitzvah. They must've bought into all those crazy rumors. Their intentions were so obvious, and at the time I couldn't believe their (here's where Gram's Yiddish comes in) chutzpah.

But the key word here is "obvious."

Now I think about Zoe looking bored during those **Doctor Who** marathons, texting her friends while we hung out, and seeming like she'd rather be in detention with Joe Lungo than doing stuff with me.

186

I'm silent as this all sinks in.

Weirdly, I don't feel so sad. I just feel dumb, like Dev said. And also ashamed. I should have seen it sooner.

I see Emmie and Sarah finish their lunches and leave.

I ignore my packed lunch of—you guessed it—cold pizza and wave bye to Dev. I hurry out just as the science kids come in. Probably for the best—I'm in no mood to talk about rock formations today.

I hurry and catch up to Emmie before I change my mind.

And stop. And hesitate. This could be harder than I thought.

I look at Emmie, a little shyly.

I notice we're right near our once-usual little hideaway meeting place.

stairwell nook

Like a reflex, we both sit on the steps at once. We watch everyone hurrying back and forth to the cafeteria.

BUT THEN I NOTICE THEY'RE NOT JUST WATCHING...

THEY'RE HERE FOR ME, WHETHER I MESS UP OR NOT. AND MOST LIKELY, I WON'T MESS UP...TOO MUCH.

THE CANTOR FINISHES THE PRAYER, AND THE RABBI GOES UP AND WELCOMES EVERYONE.

SUDDENLY, I HEAR MY NAME.

THREE WEEKS AGO

At Mom's this week. She's running errands. I'm taking advantage of the quiet evening and doing my Spanish homework.

Mom walks in, out of breath. She's holding a million bags.

Okay, I just picked up items for the out-of-towners' welcome bags. We can assemble these later.

I don't even wanna think about the bat mitzvah anymore. I just answered a Spanish question in Hebrew, and it doesn't even make sense. I think it says "Elephant breath."

Oh, it'll be over with before you know it, and you'll wish you were still in the thick of it, soaking up the attention.

Do you even know me?

I slam my Spanish book closed. And catch my fingers in it.

NO, I'm not okay! And you're right, I'm **NOT** ready! In fact, I don't even know why I'm having this stupid bat mitzvah. I never wanted it _**in the first place**_!!

I run to my room and slam the door. A couple photos flutter from my mirror frame, and my jewelry tree falls over. This condo isn't exactly the sturdiest structure.

I cry. Hard.

seven months of pent-up frustration

knock knock

I have a good cry over everything: my bickering parents (for Pete's sake, you're already divorced; stop fighting!), my nearly broken friendship with my bff, my so over friendship with a stupid user, seven months of learning prayers in an impossible language, and a yet-to-be-written speech—that has absolutely no meaning to me—which has to **knock the socks off everyone!**

I don't even have to wonder if it's worth it. It's not.

↳ probably
need an
air hole

I stay in my room for a long time before I hear knocking again.

What?

Bri, hon. Dad's here. Can we come in?

Great, she called in reinforcements. Don't know why she bothered. They'll probably end up arguing in front of me. What's frustrating is, they got along great before this whole bat mitzvah thing came about. Just another reason not to do it.

Fiiiine. I sniffle, get up, wipe the snot off my face, and open the door. My parents come in.

They chuckle, and I try not to smile at his lame dad-joke.

They look at each other.

207

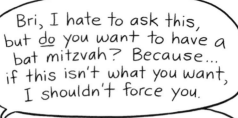

Bri, I hate to ask this, but <u>do</u> you want to have a bat mitzvah? Because... if this isn't what you want, I shouldn't force you.

I'm sorry, I realize it's so late in the game, but we can still cancel.

And don't say yes because this is some sort of big challenge you want to face, or a goal to check off.

We know you, honey.

I don't answer. I don't know what I want.

You don't have to decide right now. Sleep on it.

She smiles at me, and they head out, closing the door gently.

I flop on my back and stare at the ceiling. Even the cracks in the plaster look like Hebrew letters.

those look like "Bina"

I roll onto my stomach.

I guess I have some thinking to do.

THE CANTOR WHISPERS IN MY EAR.

Ignore them, just read. You'll be fine.

I TAKE A DEEP BREATH AND REMEMBER WHAT DEV SAID.

Once you stopped thinking so much, you were fine!

I TRY TO LISTEN TO THE CANTOR (AND DEV IN MY HEAD) AND SOMETHING HAPPENS.

something magical

remember I'm prepared

start to focus on words, not people

I MESS UP ONCE OR TWICE, BUT CANTOR CARUSO-SAGER HELPS ME.

et Adonai Elo...Elo...

...hecha

hecha

ONE WEEK AGO

School ended last week. It's been a ride.

Last day of school:

I've made some new friends and made up with an old one.

It hasn't been perfect or anything. Emmie forgave me, but I can tell she's still a little mad. She's just trying not to show it. She's hurt that I held a grudge for so long.

But it's Emmie. Which means she's really, really bad at being mad.

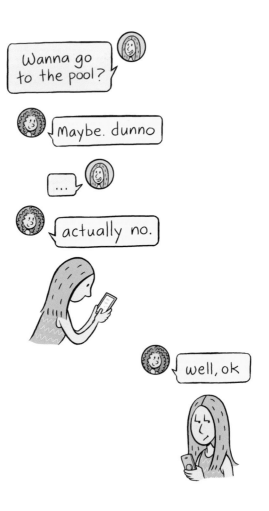

I deserve it. It's now super obvious that Zoe was just using me. She's still trying to be friendly, but I'm not having it anymore. I don't return her texts. I pretty much ignore her.

Yesterday I got tired of it and texted her back.

k ☺

I probably should confront her, but I'm too tired and crazed. Honestly, I don't even want to deal with it.

One thing I wish I could do:

My only satisfaction is knowing she realizes this isn't gonna be the blowout event she once thought it would be.

Also . . .

one week ago:

You wanted to know who was invited?

invitation list

mostly kids from Science Club, Math Club, Robotics Camp, and Dev, Emmie, and Sarah

(can practically hear their faces falling)

Meanwhile, Emmie and Sarah are still tight, which scares me. It's not that I don't like Sarah. Actually, she's grown on me . . . a lot. But I still get scared that she's gonna replace me.

Speaking of friends, I stopped talking about the bat mitzvah in front of them. I'm back to compartmentalizing, this time to the extreme. It's the only way to cope.

But yes, I'm still going through with it. I admit, a big part of it is pride. The invites were sent, I made a commitment, and I need to see it through. I also learned a buttload of Hebrew this past year, and I'm not gonna let it go to waste!

Hebrew letters

hard work and effort

meh

CLUNK

But I did think about it that night my parents talked to me. In fact, I barely slept. I realized I do want to have the bat mitzvah. Em and I video-chatted about it yesterday.

So, I realized I may not have gone to religious school all the time, I may not even _be_ religious, but there's one big thing I like about my rabbi, cantor, and temple.

What's that?

And the more I question stuff, the more I find answers I like... and don't like.

Until now, they were well-provided for while wandering in the desert. God saw to that.

But He (or She) was testing them to see if they would accept the laws when things did NOT go their way...

... when a so-called "cloud" hovered over them...

...Which makes me want to learn more.

I guess I did. Maybe someday I'll be more spiritual and stuff, maybe not—but for now, this is huge.

heavens
parting

angels singing

rabbi
clapping

I finished up the last of my Hebrew practice. The tutor just
left. I think I'm set. I give myself a mental pat on the back.

pat
pat

★ not
so
easy

But . . . I still haven't written my speech. I know, I know, stupid. I just want to get it right. I lied to everyone and said it was all

done. Besides, I **will** write it. Sometimes a last-minute deadline is the greatest motivator. That's what I tell myself, anyway.

Mom walks in the room. She's been true to her word, not bugging me about practicing or about the "big day" and stuff. She's really toned it down. That will probably change the day of, but for now, it's been helpful.

Still, I notice she smells like her favorite multipurpose cleaner. While the tutor was here, she must've been secretly deep-cleaning for the out-of-town guests.

227

She hesitates.

Well, at first I told myself it was about tradition and rite of passage and all that. But then I dove a little deeper.

What do you mean?

(sigh) I hate to admit this, but I think it became a vanity project. I wanted you to do it because _I_ did it. I wanted you to shine because _I_ wanted to shine.

Sometimes I forget that you're your own person. Or maybe a part of me resents that you and Dad have so much in common.

She suddenly smiles.

But I think that changed as you started tutoring and meeting with the clergy.

I think then it became the same reason I wanted you to do the talent show—

—to learn and grow, apart from your schoolwork. This _is_ a unique and privileged opportunity, something I wanted you to experience.

I get it.

There's more.

Her face becomes harder to read.

A bat mitzvah is about becoming part of a community. And that's something you may want to accept into your life, baby.

It was so helpful to me during the divorce.

I must have blocked it out. Or was just too busy feeling sorry for myself back then. The divorce was extra hard on my mom. She cried, like, forever. I remember hiding out at Emmie's house, holing up in our crazy little forts.

spent more time under old blankets in Em's house than in my own room

My mom runs a small performing arts camp every summer in the temple sanctuary. They put on a cute little ensemble show at the end of the four weeks. She **loves** it. I totally forgot she started that during her post-divorce mourning period. Makes sense now.

I laugh.

You can go back to your cleaning now.

My— my what?

Give up the act, Mom. I know.

And don't worry, I really don't care.

Well, then, *that's* a load off, too.

FIVE DAYS AGO

It's morning. I'm sitting on the edge of my bed, feet resting on a pile of dirty clothes. I barely slept.

You see, I made a serious

I maybe, sort of, accidentally . . . invited four extra people to my bat mitzvah—without telling my mom.

Yesterday, I was with Dev and Emmie at the pool, and we ran into Maya and Jaime. We all started hanging out, just like on the last day of school. Then Anthony and Tyler came, and we goofed around and decided to go to Taystee's afterward.

I was having so much fun (who knew?!), and in a moment of weakness . . .

I get up and start pacing my room, practicing in my head what I'm going to tell her.

This is never going to work.

I wish I could just uninvite Zoe and Olivia. At least that would open up two slots.

I stop pacing and take a deep breath. Might as well rip the Band-Aid off. I head to the kitchen, where my mom is pouring cereal in a bowl and (loudly) sipping her coffee.

I'm doomed. There's no way I can afford to pay for four extra people. I can barely afford to pay for a movie or treats with my pitiful allowance.

I head back to my room. I can hear my mom muttering under her breath.

I close my bedroom door and plop back on my bed. I try to clear all the brain cobwebs and **think**.

I'm either gonna have to take back my invitation—which would be totally **humiliating**, not to mention I'd feel so awful—or figure out a way to make some money fast.

There's no choice.

I need to brainstorm. I text Emmie and Sarah.

After all, I may have a "gifted mind" . . .
but three heads are still better than one.

(better... but not pretty)

Even so, this is a good reminder for us that you really are becoming a young woman, and this may be the moment for us to let go... a little.

I have a habit of trying to turn you into me. And your dad has a habit of thinking of you as his mini-me. It's time for us to set that aside...

... and let you be who YOU are.

Because who you are is unique and incredible, honey. And you should own that.

I now call Brianna Davis to the pulpit to give her D'var Torah, which is a speech based on the parashah, or weekly Torah portion.

I cannot believe I still haven't written my speech. What is wrong with me? Do I need some sort of speech-writing aversion therapy?

I think it stems from first grade when Miss Staci made me write an essay on glue sticks vs. squeeze bottles.

I'm at my dad's. Normally, I'd be at Mom's, but she gave up all pretense and is in the middle of deep-cleaning the entire condo.

We both decided it's best for our sanity that I stay at Dad's until Saturday.

I've been sitting on my bed for, like, half an hour, trying to write this speech. I need to do it before Dad comes home. (He still thinks I wrote the darn thing.)

But my mind wanders . . . again.

I think back to a few days ago.

Emmie, Sarah, and I had a group text. They offered to chip in for the four dinners, but I said no way.

how bout mowing neighbors' lawns?

I'd probably lose a toe. or ten.

u could fill out online surveys like my sister. oh wait. u have to be 18.

we need a book on get-rich-quick schemes!

That's when an idea hit. Books!

During the next few hours, I ran back and forth between my mom's house, my dad's, Em's, and Sarah's. We all gathered as many books and clothes as we could and dumped them in the middle of my room.

There was a TON.

Wow.

LOTS of old clothes

Harry Potter costume

wand

old reading assignments, some textbooks, a few fun one-and-done books

I told Mom about the plan and asked if she would help. Luckily, she enthusiastically agreed.

So we drove to the used bookstore.

I groan. Not enough. But it helps.

covers almost half a person

Then we drove to the consignment shop.

I can give you $8 for these.

now covers 4/5 of a person

ahh!

(or 1 headless person)

Plan B. When I got home, I started rummaging through my bookshelf. In the fall, Emmie and I took a babysitting class at the YMCA, and we collected a bunch of phone numbers afterward from neighborhood parents. We were determined to make a pile of money during the school year. Em managed to snag a few jobs, but me . . .

Found it!

filled with neighborhood phone numbers

sticker-riddled folder

GAKK!

(I really need to clean that shelf)

I scanned all the numbers and chose a bunch that I thought would be a good fit. I texted the parents.

Hi [blank]. This is Brianna Davis from Olive St. Going into 8th grade. We talked in the fall.
Just wanted to let you know I'm available for babysitting on nights and weekends!! Please call or text this # if your interested.

Argh!!

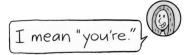

I mean "you're."

My English-teaching mom would have a fit.

Only one person responded. BUT—I have a babysitting job lined up after the bat mitzvah.

I can cover the rest with some of my bat mitzvah gift money, and then put it back in my savings as soon as I get enough babysitting cash.

Again, Mom enthusiastically agreed.

It's not the ideal situation, but it works.

I snap out of my daydream and try to focus again. The speech!

My dad knocks and peeks in before I can say anything.

He catches himself. Dad doesn't like to be one of those parents who flies off the handle.

I sit up.

I start penning furiously. It's about time.

He closes the door.

I'm finally dumping! An avalanche! Well, maybe a couple big pieces of rock, but it's a start.

I write and write until Dad calls me for dinner.

"All that the Eternal has spoken, we will do."

That's what the Israelites said to Moses when he gave them their new laws.

They didn't even hesitate. They just obeyed.

And that's exactly what I did when I finally agreed to have a bat mitzvah.

ha ha haha

"But the coach gave his players a pep talk. He said that each of the competing players was a superstar. BUT that they were only out for themselves."

"He said that the way to beat 'em was to look out for each other and play as a team."

"So his team played with total cooperation, and soon the game was tied."

"In the end, one player wanted to make the final winning shot and be a hero."

"But he remembered his coach's words and passed the ball to his team-mate, who had a better chance of making the shot."

"And guess what? Yup,
they won!"

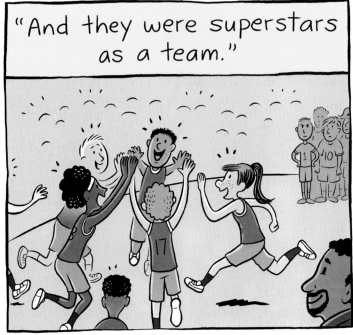

"And they were superstars
as a team."

When the Israelites received the laws at Mount Sinai, they stood together with a feeling of unity. It's this unity that I think compelled them to obey the laws without hesitation.

They were in it together!

Luckily, it turned out they were told to do good things. They were told to respect each other and look out for each other, to be a community.

Yeah, that sure goes against my nature. But I did it when I joined a talent show. I made a new friend out of it. I did it when I made up with my bff after a fight, something I was very stubborn about.

giggle

Some of this leap-of-faith stuff didn't work out so well, but most did.

I did it when my dad encouraged me to brain-dump this speech and figure out the meaning after. I've never brain-dumped anything! Ha HA

NOW

We're all back in the atrium, snacking on little appetizers. The cantor just led a totally beautiful havdalah ceremony, marking the end of Shabbat (Sabbath), which is sundown Friday to sundown Saturday.

Shavua Tov, Shavua Tov...

havdalah candle

extinguishes
it in wine

Now I'm in full-fledged relief mode.

almost
giddy

kinda
buzzing

But I still have to be "on" 'cause people are congratulating me
left and right.

goes on and on and on and on

Also, I'm so hungry, I just asked (okay, ordered) Dev to grab some snacks for me.

The doors suddenly open—loudly—and I see Zoe and Olivia walk in, dressed to the nines.

I can't believe it. They didn't even come to the service; they just came for the party!

I shake my head. I'm momentarily angry, but I **won't** let this ruin anything.

The rabbi walks over, a stuffed grape leaf shoved in his mouth. Guess I'm not the only hungry one.

Thankfully, he swallows the appetizer before he speaks.

284

I'm still chuckling at my mom, who rolls her eyes.
Guess we aren't so different after all.

MY MOM OPENS THE DOORS TO THE PARTY ROOM. DANCE MUSIC SPILLS OUT.

It's party time, Bri. Wanna lead the way?

Yeah!

Wait. Someone wants to walk in with you.

Where's Sarah?

She's with the others. I wanted to come myself.

Why?

It's a surprise.

IT'S FILLED WITH BOOKS! LITERALLY!

STEM GIRLZ

The Witch & The Wizardess

101 Science Factoids

DID U KNOW?

huge painted books (my faves!) on fabric

books stacked as centerpieces!

candy

confetti

LIBRARY

wel co me

library photo backdrop!

IT'S TRADITION TO DO A GOOD DEED AS PART OF A BAT MITZVAH.

had guests buy and bring new books for "Books for Kids"

Please deposit books here

Bri's

Bookish

Bat

Mi

I asked some of my stage-crew students to help me with the backdrops.

And while the guests arrived, Emmie took the donations and made these centerpieces.

That's why I was late to the service. Sorry.

PEOPLE ENTER THE ROOM.
THEY GASP, JUST LIKE I DID.

I thought you were still a little mad at me.

I was... for a while. An' I know you're not always so crazy about Sarah.

But she's the one who kept telling me you're my best friend and it's time to get over it.

That's what Dev kept saying.

ha ha

But...you **are** still my best friend, right?

What do **you** think?

I LOOK AGAIN — AT THE DECORATIONS, AT EVERYONE'S EXCITEMENT, AND AT EM'S HOPEFUL FACE.

ooo ahhh!

EPILOGUE

I'm having a fun time, for sure. My friends and I have already danced our buns off.

We took a little break to eat (pizza and pasta!), ogle the sundae bar, and rest our feet (buh-bye, shoes!), but now we're back on the dance floor. If there's one thing thirteen-year-olds can do, it's dance all night.

The DJ's a little corny, but I think he got the hint and has finally laid off the bad jokes. Anyway, he plays good music, and that's the important part.

The best thing is watching all the grown-ups get down. This is probably the only time I'm not embarrassed by horrible dancing.

Not including the cantor. Who knew she had moves!

I notice Zoe and Olivia are keeping to themselves. They came up to me earlier and said congrats, but that was about it. They're not besties with Jaime, Maya, Anthony, and Tyler, but they run in the same sort of crowd. Still . . . it almost looks like they're avoiding everyone.

We laugh. I had told them how those crafty girls used me to score an invite.

But I stop laughing when I look back over at Zoe and Olivia. They watch us awkwardly while sitting and nibbling on some candy that my mom had scattered on the tables.

If I didn't know their motives, I'd feel sorry for them. This is the first time I've seen them look totally out of place.

I guess "cool" depends on context. And if their regular context is "school," then they are way out of their environment.

My thoughts are interrupted as Dev does a bizarre imitation of a moonwalk over to me.

308

The song ends. Something is nagging at my gut. I glance over at Zoe and Olivia again, who look miserable or bored or both.

Before I can talk myself out of it, I walk over to them.

They look surprised but also grateful. They get up to follow me, then Zoe stops and taps me on the arm.

I lead them to my circle of friends. It's weird seeing Zoe and Olivia so awkward. And my friends are kinda frosty. But I smile and start to dance. Everyone follows my lead, and my friends start to smile and dance, too. I guess they figure if a grudge holder like me can forgive those two, so can they.

310

Soon I'm having so much fun, I almost don't notice when the song ends and the DJ picks up the mike.

All you danceaholics! Stop what you're doing because it's time for...

... the hora!

Everyone form a circle!

"Hava Nagila" song

Before I can think, someone grabs a chair from one of the tables, and my aunt Dani coaxes me into it. Suddenly I'm lifted up, up, up—almost to the ceiling! I scream, half from excitement, half from pure terror. My dad, uncle Ryan, cousin Bradley, and one of my dad's teacher friends have each grabbed a chair leg and lifted me over the crowd!

The music plays loudly, and the crowd dances and cheers in a circle around me while I bob up and down. Even the ones who don't know the hora have caught on fast (it's not complicated).

What was it that I said to Dev?

Me and my big mouth!

A "BAT MITZVAH" GLOSSARY

In case you haven't been to a bar or bat mitzvah, here's a helpful guide to some unfamiliar phrases.

Bar or Bat Mitzvah: This means son or daughter of the commandments. It signifies the coming of age in the Jewish community and becoming responsible for the performance of **mitzvot** . . . (plural of mitzvah), or duties of Jewish life.

You can have a bar or bat mitzvah at any time in your life [author's note: my in-laws had theirs when they were in their sixties!] although it's most common to have one around age thirteen. These days, non-binary kids sometimes call their ceremony a b'nai mitzvah (b'nai is plural and can refer to a mixed-gender group of people).

Bimah: A raised platform, pulpit, or podium where Jewish services are conducted.

Cantor: A Jewish religious official who leads the musical part of a service.

D'var Torah: A talk based on topics relating to a parashah, or Torah portion.

Havdalah Ceremony: Marks the conclusion of the Sabbath (Friday sundown to Saturday sundown). This consists of blessings over wine, bread, and the light of a candle.

Hebrew language (biblical): ancient native language of Israel.

Hora: A Jewish circle dance, usually done at celebrations like weddings and bar or bat mitzvahs. The music for the dance is "Hava Nagila," an Israeli folk song that means "Let us rejoice." It's customary to raise the honorees on chairs during the hora.

Parashah: A portion of the Torah that is recited every week until the entire Torah is read in a year's time.

Rabbi: A Jewish leader, scholar, or teacher. Usually the chief religious official of a synagogue.

Synagogue: A place of Jewish worship. Many also call it a temple or a shul.

Torah: A sacred handwritten parchment scroll that contains all the prayers and laws of the Jewish people. It is written in Hebrew.

Yarmulke: Also called a kippah; a head covering (looks like a beanie) worn by Jewish men and sometimes women. It is a sign of reverence. It's often worn when reading from the Torah.

ACKNOWLEDGMENTS:

Brianna was a joy to create, and it couldn't have been done without my invaluable support team:

Donna Bray, my wise and intuitive editor, who can coax the best ideas out of me, even when they're buried in the back of my mind.

Dan Lazar, my fearless, kind, and supportive agent, who always has my back.

Laura Mock and Dana Fritts at HarperCollins, who are skilled at fitting together these puzzle pieces that are the art and text of my books. You rock!

Everyone at HarperCollins who has had a hand in the Emmie and Friends series. You're the best!

Rabbi Josh Caruso, who helped me in the early stages of this book and inspired much of its meaningful content.

My family—Mike, Mollie, and Nikki—who surround me with love, support, and bags of potato chips when I lose it.

My mom and siblings—Meral, Brad, and Tina—who are my creative cheerleaders and always spread the word about my books (whether I like it or not).

Aaron, who is no longer with us but I'm sure is rooting for Brianna from above.

Mina, my sister from another mister, who I always ~~ask~~ force to read my manuscripts, and whose opinion I trust.

And, as always, my readers, who make this the ultimate dream job!